The Canine Commandments

The Canine Commandments

Kendal Shepherd BVSc., CCAB, MRCVS
Illustrated by Victor Ambrus

Acknowledgements

Special thanks to:
Ian Dunbar for his inimitable inspiration
Danny Mills for getting the writing started
Richard Hall and Julie Clubley of Hawthorn Primary School for allowing year 6's to be used as guinea pigs
Wendy King for her constant nagging for the finished article
Karen Overall for her invaluable advice and constructive criticism
Aidan Shepherd for his patience during frequent attacks of computer rage
and Rod for everything.

Also of course to Victor Ambrus for his wonderfully sensitive and humorous drawings
and Catherine Mason of Broadcast Books for her support and enthusiasm.

This book is written for everyone but is dedicated to Linden and all children who have been bitten by dogs, and who will continue to get bitten, until our understanding of the nature of dogs matches our need for their company.

Published by Broadcast Books
84 Whiteladies Road, Bristol BS8 2QP
catherine@broadcastbooks.co.uk
www.broadcastbooks.co.uk
Tel: 0117 923 8891

Designed by Martin Laurie
martinlaurie@ukonline.co.uk
Tel: 01925 757 864

Printed and bound by
Bath Press, Lower Bristol Road, Bath

Isbn: 978 1 874092 55 1

Contents

Introduction for parents

Up to 200,000 dog bites are reported annually in the UK, well over half of them being inflicted upon the face and hands of children. Estimates of bites requiring hospital attention vary world-wide from 118 per 100,000 people per year in the UK to 573 per 100,000 people per year in the USA. Contrary to popular belief, the majority of these bites occur at home and involve children and a dog known to them, usually their own. In addition to this alarmingly large number of reported bites, there is a very great number of unreported incidences involving damaging bites inflicted upon owners and their families and friends, who are unwilling to admit that the dog they love and live with could behave like this. Then there are the nips not requiring medical attention, as well as snaps and growls.

Recent studies, which include information about such non-reported bites as well as those requiring medical attention, confirm an incidence of bites in children under the age of 15 years as high as 2,200 per 100,000 individuals. They also show that the vast majority of dog bites occurring at home resulted during interactions which were initiated by the child, strongly suggesting that if the child had not behaved in a certain way, the dog would not have bitten. The intense media attention received by apparently unprovoked and fatal dog attacks gives a falsely exaggerated impression of the risks dogs pose. These tragic but rare incidents are almost invariably caused by ill-advised human action, or rather lack of it: the simple absence of competent adult supervision in the presence of an animal capable of serious harm. If dogs are deliberately selected or trained to attack people, this is an abuse of the fundamentally trusting and compatible relationship that dogs have with us.

But how similar to our everyday human aggression – in the form of angry words or thrown objects – is the canine growl or the snap? In people as well as in dogs, aggression is an external expression of internal conflict, and arises out of a complex mix of instinctive and learned responses to the environment. Therefore learning how to live safely and in harmony with dogs, whether in the same house or merely in the same street, involves learning about ourselves, and this is a process best begun in childhood – although these lessons are of course equally applicable to adults. After all, much of what children suffer at the teeth of dogs is previously created, in both dog and child, by adults.

Increasing a child's understanding of dogs, in order to change the way they behave towards them, should significantly reduce the risk of bites, in much the same way as the Green Cross Code (or 'how to behave around traffic') was introduced to prevent road accidents. Any child old enough to understand the significance of the word 'please' is well able to get to grips with the concepts and principles in this book, particularly if they are encouraged to reflect on their own experiences and reactions in various situations, and then try to predict how dogs may similarly feel and respond.

There are marked social similarities between a group of playing children and a group of dogs. Without realising it, children will constantly use reciprocal gestures and facial expressions to initiate, maintain or reject social contact and interaction with each other. In this way, each child maintains the level of social contact within the group with which they feel at ease, and so harmony and stability are generally maintained. Such gestures have nothing to do with indicating rank or status and are expressed identically by individuals of all social backgrounds. They therefore enable people from all walks of life and experience to communicate effectively with each other and minimise misunderstandings.

Exactly the same is true for dogs. The concept of a 'pack leader' informing others of what to do, frequently by violent means, is unfortunately entrenched in the public perception as an essential need for the modern day domestic dog. This concept should however be restricted to wild dogs, which have not been modified by thousands of years of both natural and artificial selection to become so uniquely adapted to human society. Dogs, as children, need companionship, affection, understanding and consistency in their relationships with us, rather than aggressively asserted leadership.

Social gestures in both dog and man are largely genetically driven, but they require lots of rehearsal in order for individual children and dogs to become 'socially polished'. The extent to which each individual enjoys or can cope with social interaction depends upon character traits as well as their previous experiences. The exact meaning of certain gestures may vary between human cultures and may lead to misunderstanding. In dogs, selective breeding, such as for a short nose, wrinkled skin or staring eyes, may adversely affect the ability of certain breeds to use parts of the body to signal and can therefore limit their ability to be understood by their companions, whether human or canine. One most important anatomical feature, the tail, cannot be used at all if it is removed and docked according to the dictate of human fashion.

Some human gestures do not come naturally, for example, shaking hands and saying 'please' and 'thank you'. They are however taught, as soon as a child is old enough to learn, so that they are able to put other people at ease in social situations. A canine equivalent to the human handshake as a social opening gambit is to 'sit to greet'. This is already present in the canine repertoire, but must be consistently reinforced from puppyhood if we want to create a far more pleasing animal than one who continues to jump up as an adult. Both children and dogs learn that socially acceptable gestures are a good way of getting others to be nice to you and achieving what you want out of life! Politeness and manners have become cultural norms for both humans and dogs simply because they are so useful.

To guide children, and, of course, the adults they live with, to interact more safely with dogs, the following set of *'Canine Commandments'* has been developed. They are simple to understand and relevant to all children, whether they already live with a dog or not. They are followed by the canine *Ladder of Aggression*, an illustrated representation of the escalation of gestures dogs will use, if their attempts to keep the peace are ignored or misunderstood. The Ladder culminates in growling, snapping and biting. No children who have thoroughly learnt the *Canine Commandments* should put themselves in a position where there is a risk of being bitten, regardless of a dog's previous experiences of people and the world. At the same time, the dogs they come into contact with will be relieved of potentially unwelcome social pressure and have little, if any, need to bite. As a result, both children and their canine companions will have considerably calmer and more content relationships.

I am indebted to Victor Ambrus for his enthusiasm for the subject, embodied in his humorous yet accurate interpretation and illustration of the text.

Kendal Shepherd, BVSc., CCAB, MRCVS 2007

Being cross does not make you the boss

1

Although all our pet dogs are descended from the wolf, the dogs we know today no longer function in packs like wolves do. Instead of hunting for a living, the dog has developed as a scavenger of waste that man has thrown away and therefore does not need to have a single leader or 'top dog'. Although dogs still very much enjoy chasing things, such as balls, sticks and rabbits, they no longer have to work together to kill and eat what they chase. If a group of dogs run together chasing the same thing, it is because it is an enjoyable and sociable thing to do, in much the same way as playing a game of football, rather than the means of getting dinner. One of the reasons we get along so well with dogs is that they are very much like us and need to live as we do – as a family or in a group of friends.

Just as they no longer have to chase in order to kill and eat, dogs do not use aggression to make themselves the boss. Unfortunately, however, many people still believe that an angry and aggressive dog is trying to be bossy and be the 'top dog'. They also believe that, in order to make themselves 'the boss', they have to behave in a bossy and aggressive manner towards their dogs. This is not only untrue but extremely dangerous.

If dogs or people get angry and aggressive, it is because they feel threatened. It is not because they are 'the boss', nor does it make them be 'the boss'. Imagine yourself in a dog's position. If someone continues to shout or be angry with you, despite your saying sorry or trying to calm him or her down, you will eventually feel you need to be angry in return. Whether you win your argument or not will depend upon what the other person decides to do. He or she may change their mind and agree with you or they may continue to argue and fight. Whatever the eventual result, being angry does not make either person 'the boss'.

A truly superior dog is actually a very calm and confident individual who very rarely has to get cross or aggressive with anyone. The best way for your dog to think that you are also superior and can be trusted to make good decisions, is to remain very calm when you are with him and not to play with him just because he seems to want to. Instead you must show him clearly *what you need him to do without getting angry. If we get cross, a dog will automatically think that we are not reliable or trustworthy. They will also become upset and anxious and may even feel the need to defend themselves by growling and biting.*

Any dog may bite if he feels in danger

ou may have seen grownups getting angry with a dog, or trying to push or pull a dog into doing what they want him to do. **Do not copy them!** Forcing dogs to do something they do not want to is one of the main reasons why dogs bite us. It also explains why the hand or arm is the most frequently bitten part of our bodies. Dogs do not start out wanting to bite us but the way we sometimes behave makes them feel in danger. In exactly the same way, there may be times when you have an argument with a friend or brother or sister and end up having a fight. You did not want it to end up this way and would have preferred for your friend or brother to agree with you instead. We have our voices, words and hands to argue and fight with. Dogs only have their teeth.

Dogs often feel they have to bite when we accidentally misunderstand what they are trying to tell us with their body language. We are able to say with words, 'Stop that, I don't like it', and most of the time we are understood by people around us without having to get upset or angry. Dogs use their bodies to 'speak' to other dogs and us. If a dog walks away from you, he is simply saying 'I feel a bit worried being close to you'. If he turns his head away as you try to put his collar on or pull him off the sofa, he is saying 'You are making me feel worried and threatened'. If you walk towards him to try to make him come to you or continue to pull him, you are 'starting an argument' as far as the dog is concerned which may well end in tears or worse. If we want to get on well with our dogs, we must never threaten them or make ourselves appear dangerous to them.

Whether a dog feels in danger or not also depends upon what has happened to him in the past and how used he is to things around him. Although we know that trains, planes, people with funny hats on, the postman and the vet are not dangerous, we cannot assume that our dogs also know this. In much the same way as people hate going to the dentist, because they are afraid that it will hurt, dogs become afraid of things they think may hurt them. The fact that a vet does not want to hurt a dog makes no difference to what the dog thinks. Quite simply, if a dog cannot run away when he is frightened, because he is trapped in a room or on lead, he may well bite. Dogs need to be taught that the world and things in it are nice. If he is given goodies while being patted and hugged by all sorts of different people, he will learn to enjoy this attention. If hands are used to reward rather than punish him, then hands become good news rather than bad.

Never hit or kick a dog

3

There are two main purposes for which people try to discipline a dog using their hands or feet. We either use such punishments to force dogs to do things we want them to or to stop them doing things we don't want them to. For example, we may push a dog to sit or lie down if he hasn't done what he's told or we may feel like smacking a dog for chewing our shoes or for weeing in the sitting room. We may not actually even want to hit a dog but instead, use the threat of a raised hand or foot to say to the dog, 'Do it or else!' or 'Don't you dare!'

Punishment is unfortunately very much part of the way we humans deal with each other. We think that if we threaten a person with going to prison, or actually send them to prison, it will, for example, teach them not to steal cars in the future. Also, we assume that dogs, as well as people, automatically know the difference between right and wrong. There is very little evidence to show that this approach is effective with people, let alone with dogs. Punishment for both people and dogs ends up as being a 'tit for tat' system – 'You've done something horrid to me, I'm angry so I'm going to do something horrid to you back' – rather than teaching what should be done instead of being 'bad'. By punishing dogs when we are angry, a dog may learn only that hands, feet and angry human voices are dangerous and that he might get hurt. If a dog expects danger, he may bite.

The only lesson a dog is ever likely to learn if we hit them is that we ourselves might become dangerous at certain times and should be avoided at all costs. He certainly does not learn that bones should be chewed rather than shoes and that he should wee in the garden in future rather than indoors. You must remember that the next time you want to walk up to a dog and stroke him because you are happy and pleased rather than cross, how is he supposed to know the difference? If you or anyone else ever teaches a dog that hands or feet are 'bad news' and may hurt, then he may end up wanting to bite them all the time.

Do not touch a dog you don't know

Although we may like dogs and want to be friendly towards them, what we do to try to be friendly may be looked on very differently by a dog. A hug and a kiss from your Mum or Dad or a friend is an enjoyable experience. But you would not want to be kissed, hugged, or even touched by everyone, particularly if you don't know them. Dogs are exactly the same. If a dog has not yet met a person who looks, sounds and smells like you do, or if he remembers something nasty about someone who looks, sounds or smells like you, he will not want you to touch him. He may just turn his head away or decide to walk away from you. He may, however, think that snapping at you or biting is the safest thing to do.

Never go up to a dog tied up in the street and touch him even if he looks as if he's pleased to see you. It is always safest to walk past calmly without staring at the dog. If a dog is being walked by his owner, again you must walk calmly and slowly towards them and only touch the dog if the owner says that you can. Do not assume that patting and hugs, or even being looked at, are things that dogs automatically enjoy. The excitement dogs may show when we approach them is their way of saying that they do not want to harm us and certainly do not want us to harm them. We should think of it as meaning 'Please don't threaten me' rather than 'Please hug and pat me'. Dogs do however enjoy knowing exactly what they are supposed to do. Asking a dog to sit and giving him a food reward is a much better way of saying 'Hello' than patting him.

Do not tease or deliberately excite a dog

5

What do we mean by the word 'tease'? Whether you are teasing a friend, your sister or brother or your dog, teasing involves holding onto something on purpose, something that you know they want. You may be teasing a friend by saying 'I know something you don't know!' or your brother by refusing to share your sweets with him or your dog by showing him his ball and then not letting him have it. To a certain extent, training a dog or your younger brother involves a little 'teasing', and we use what we know dogs and people want, to teach them things. The dog can have the ball he wants as long as he sits nicely and your brother needs to learn to say 'please' first, if he wants one of your sweets.

What we must not do however, is keep either your dog or brother waiting so long that they become very excited, upset or angry. It may seem like fun to work a dog up into excitement, particularly when they are puppies, but you will not teach the right lessons if you do. It may even be dangerous to you when they grow into much bigger dogs. No-one can think clearly when they are over-excited or angry. Instead of learning to sit calmly for a ball, the dog may jump up or even grab your hand or arm instead of the ball. Your brother may burst into tears or try to hit you. On the other hand, a calm dog, or brother for that matter, very rarely causes us any trouble.

One of the main times that dogs learn to be excited is when we come home and they seem to want to say hello to us. Such excitement may make us feel that our dogs love us and we automatically want to hug and pat them. However, attention from us when they are excited accidentally teaches our dogs that excitement is a good thing. If you do not mind your dog jumping up, scratching you and putting muddy paws all over you then by all means continue to say hello when he is excited. But you will create behaviour which is unpleasant and dangerous for others. It may even endanger your dog's life as dogs are not allowed by law to hurt or even to frighten people. If, however, you would prefer your dog to be calm and polite, then you must turn away and ignore excited greetings. Simply do not say hello until a dog is calm and quiet and will sit when you ask him to.

Dogs do not know the difference between right and wrong

We, as humans, are taught very early in our lives what is considered to be 'good' behaviour and what is thought to be 'bad'. We are taught to say please and thank you, to shake hands, and that things need to be paid for rather than stolen. We also learn that it is better to be nice to other people rather than to try to hurt them. Through this teaching, we develop an idea of what is 'right' (or 'good'), and 'wrong' (or 'bad').

If a dog chews up our shoes, steals food from the fridge, or bites the postman, we are all in agreement that this is 'bad' behaviour. But does the dog know that it is 'wrong' to do these things? At other times, we think that our dogs have been 'good', maybe because they performed particularly well in training class, or have waited until we get home before having a wee, or because they come running straight back to us in the park the minute we call them. But how do they know that these are the 'right' things to do? Do they think of them as 'right' at all? In other words, what does 'right' and 'wrong' mean if you happen to be a dog?

The reality is that dogs have simply no idea of our human concepts of right or wrong and certainly do not choose what to do based on whether we think their behaviour is **good** or **bad**. All they are thinking is that some things, like chasing balls or rabbits, are **exciting** and some things are **boring**, like walking to heel or staying at home alone. Things they do may also seem to be **safe**, like having a wee in the sitting-room or chewing shoes when they are alone, or **dangerous**, like having a wee in the sitting-room or chewing shoes if someone catches them at it. In other words, a dog decides what to do based on what usually happens afterwards, rather than whether he thinks he is being good or bad. If we are not very careful, by getting angry we may actually teach our dogs that it is safer to run away from us and chase rabbits and to wait until we have gone out to wee or chew things in the house. Instead, what we should be teaching is that it is always safe, exciting and rewarding to come back to us and to wee and chew where and what we want. What a dog views as safe, exciting and rewarding will then also seem to us to be 'good'.

Unfortunately for dogs, they are very good at looking as if they know they have done something wrong when we are angry with them. They may crouch down, lay their ears back and tuck their tail tightly under their tummy or they may even run away from us. But all they are really saying is 'Please calm down!' If you get angry with a guilty-looking dog, you will only teach him that it is very dangerous to chew or wee when you are around. He will therefore learn that he must wait until you are not there to chew or wee in peace rather than that chewing or weeing is 'wrong'. You may even teach him to bite you.

Behaviours that dogs enjoy will be repeated

Anything a dog does which has a good outcome for him will be repeated, such as walking by your side in exchange for a food treat or bringing a ball back to be thrown again for him. However, what you look and sound like must stay the same, regardless of where you are, if you want your dog to continue to behave in the same way. If the sound of dog's name and the sight of a beckoning hand always mean, 'Food available if you run in this direction', then a dog will become very obedient when called. For a dog to really believe in this 'good news', then you must practise everywhere you expect the dog to obey you. If food only appears in training class or in the kitchen but not in the garden or park, then your dog will only believe you are worth obeying in training class or the kitchen. If a dog is called angrily, with a frown and pointed finger rather than a jolly voice, a smile and wave, and then gets a smack when he comes because he has 'done something wrong', he may well decide, very sensibly, to run away from you instead next time. Your body must always look like good news if your dog is really to trust and believe in you.

We often assume that dogs will do as we want just because we will be happy and praise them. But our own pleasure does not necessarily matter to a dog. Dogs of course want to be happy, as we do, and, like us, will do things to create a feeling of happiness. But problems arise when what makes a dog happy, and what makes us happy, differ. A dog may enjoy chewing your shoes, but is this what you are happy with? We may enjoy patting a dog on the head to praise him, but is this what he would like the best? A chew toy stuffed with food will give your dog pleasure and you the chance to praise your dog for chewing the right thing rather than getting cross with him. To train your dog properly, always consider what makes him happy as well as yourself. Let him have what makes him happy as a result of doing something for you. If a dog gets what he wants when we are pleased with him, then he will be happy to please us. The aim of any relationship between a dog and a person is that both of you should be happy at exactly the same time!

8 Dogs must be taught what you want them to do and they must choose to do it

Most dogs, when introduced to our houses and the way we live, whether as a puppy or adult, are given the idea that they can do exactly as they please until they do something that makes us angry. They are allowed to roam all over the house until they wee in the bedroom and then they are confined downstairs. They are allowed to jump up to say hello until they grow bigger and hurt someone and then they are smacked for jumping up. Instead of showing them exactly what we want them to do right from the start, we wait until they do something wrong and then we get cross with them. This is, quite simply, a very inefficient, upsetting and stressful way to teach or learn anything.

Imagine if your teacher, instead of explaining how to do a sum or spell a particular word, just shouted at you or hit you for every mistake. Would you enjoy being at school? Would you enjoy learning? Would you in fact learn anything at all? However horrible this sounds, this is exactly what most dogs have to put up with every day.

We all know what we don't want dogs to do. We know that we don't want them to bite people, they shouldn't run away in the park, we don't want them to chew our belongings and they certainly shouldn't use the sitting-room as a toilet. But are we doing enough to show them what we do want? Have we even decided what we want them to do? Before any dog can become 'obedient' to us, we must decide exactly what we want them to do – not just what we don't want them to. We must then make what we want them to do more exciting, safe and rewarding than anything else. Running towards you when you call, or having a wee in the garden rather than indoors, will be both safe and fun for your dog if you give a food treat or a toy as a reward. If we have patience and take enough time to do this, dogs will then choose for themselves to listen to us and to do as we ask.

Do not take anything away from a dog

Whatever a dog has in his mouth, he must choose to give it to you rather than you try to take it away by force. Dogs have evolved as scavenging animals, which have in the past needed to guard food from others in order to survive. They are therefore much more selfish than we would often like them to be and guarding behaviour can be very important to them. We may guard something by telling people to stay away or putting a 'KEEP OUT!' sign up on the door of our room or gate. Dogs can only do it by walking away from us and growling or biting.

Dogs often seem to steal our favourite or most useful things. This is because doing so always seems to get us the most excited and results in dogs getting lots of attention from us. Socks, pairs of knickers, your toys, tea towels and the TV remote control are always the best bet as far as a dog is concerned! If you follow your dog to try to get the object back, not only will he think you are joining in a chase game but he may begin to feel threatened. What do dogs do if they are feeling threatened? **Bite!**

Your dog must always be given a very good reason to drop what he has in his mouth. If coming to you always means he gets a tasty piece of food, he will love running towards you. If opening his mouth to drop what is inside it means the food gets even tastier, he will love to bring things to you and drop them. If you are angry and chase him, however, he may learn that he has to bite you.

When dogs are being 'bad', they need the most help, not the most punishment

Whenever a dog does something 'bad', in reality, all he has done is upset us. Looking at it the other way round, if we are not upset by what dogs do, then we do not consider their behaviour to be bad. Your Mum may hate your dog barking all the time but the old lady who lives on her own down the road may feel very safe if her dog barks a lot whenever someone passes by or comes to the door. Although an aggressive dog is thought to be 'dangerous' and 'bad', many people like their dogs to be 'protective' of them and their property. What is the difference between being protective and aggressive if you are a dog? Very little, most of the time! But we as humans like it sometimes and reward it, and hate it at other times and try to punish it.

All the things that dogs do are the obvious choices as far as they are concerned. Although we may think they are being bad or naughty, they are likely to be thinking:

"That postman looks dangerous, I must chase him away."

"That rubbish bin smells great, I must tip it over and find what's inside."

"My bladder's full, it's raining and no-one's looking, so I'll just nip behind the sofa."

So we must help dogs to avoid doing things that upset us and make us angry, rather than simply calling them 'bad' dogs, punishing them and expecting them to automatically understand what we want. The truth is that the worse a dog behaves, the harder he is finding it to make the right decision from our point of view. We must therefore think how easy or difficult it is for a dog to do what we ask – not how good or bad we think he is – and we must pay them accordingly. The rewards we have on offer for our dogs must be something that is valuable to them and that they really want. We must be prepared to reward them well for doing what we want – however long it takes and without getting impatient or angry. The longer a dog takes to understand and do as we ask, the greater the reward he deserves for his effort and achievement. If we become angry instead, he may never learn what we really want him to do. He may also learn to bite us.

Get your dog used to your life

11

A dog does not need to learn that certain things in the environment are frightening. He does not need something nasty to have happened to him to be afraid of wheelie bins or small children, for example. Being afraid is just the way many dogs automatically feel if they have not met or experienced something before in their lives. The most important time for dogs to get used to things is when they are puppies, as this is when their brain is best able to learn good news about the world. By the time a young dog is six months old, he is the equivalent of a teenager. He must have learnt about almost everything he is expected to cope with later in your life by this age.

There is also no point is getting a dog used to someone else's life. A dog must get used to how **you** live and what **you** expect of him. If a dog has been brought up on a farm, he may be able to cope with and be friendly towards people in Wellington boots, sheep, cows, tractors and his own littermates, but this will not help him with joggers wearing trainers, skateboarders, trains, planes and strange dogs in the park. Although we think of working dogs, such as sheep dogs and gun dogs, as very clever and well-trained, the pet dogs we have in our houses need to be even better at doing all sorts of different things. We need them to be happy on their own and happy with lots of people. We need them to tolerate being poked and prodded by show judges and vets. We need them to bark at burglars but not at our friends. We need them to chew **their** toys but not **our** toys. We need them to do exactly what we want them to do but often do not take the time to show them exactly what these things are. The younger a dog is when he is introduced to all aspects of your life and taught what you need him to do, the better.

Teach your dog to say 'please'

12

Just as we are taught that it is polite to ask for things that we need and want rather than merely helping ourselves, dogs should also learn that things they want and enjoy in life need to be asked for nicely. Sometimes they also need to learn to wait a while for things they want, without expecting results immediately. Many dogs have been allowed to think that they can help themselves to anything they want and that the more annoying their behaviour is to us, the better it works in getting our attention! This is a bad mistake to make.

A very useful doggy equivalent of 'please' is to sit quietly when asked. If from a very young age, a puppy is asked to sit before he is given anything at all that he wants, including games and cuddles as well as bits of food, a 'sit' will become his most useful behaviour – if you like, his 'magic' word! The word 'sit' can then be used successfully later to stop lots of things that we don't like, such as jumping up, barking, and even biting. You can even use it to impress your friends! Just as we say 'please' however old we get, a dog should continue to practise sitting throughout his life. Equally, we do not expect the word 'please' to only work at certain times and places or even to stop working at all – nor should the 'sit' behaviour. So make sure your dog is given something nice for sitting everywhere he goes and whatever else is happening. There is no better way to make sure your dog gets used to the world and, at the same time, learns to do as you ask everywhere.

The Ladder of Agression

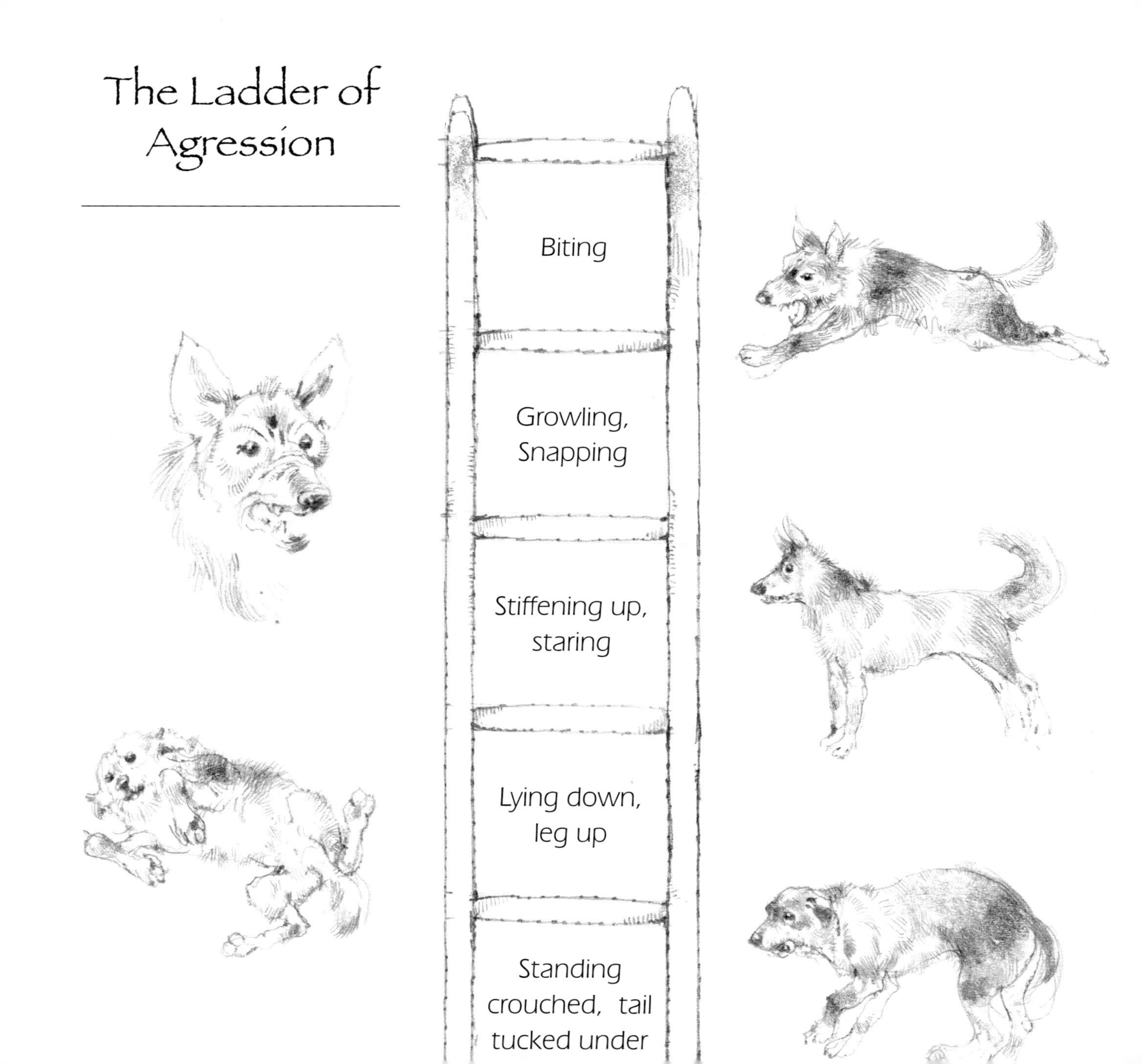

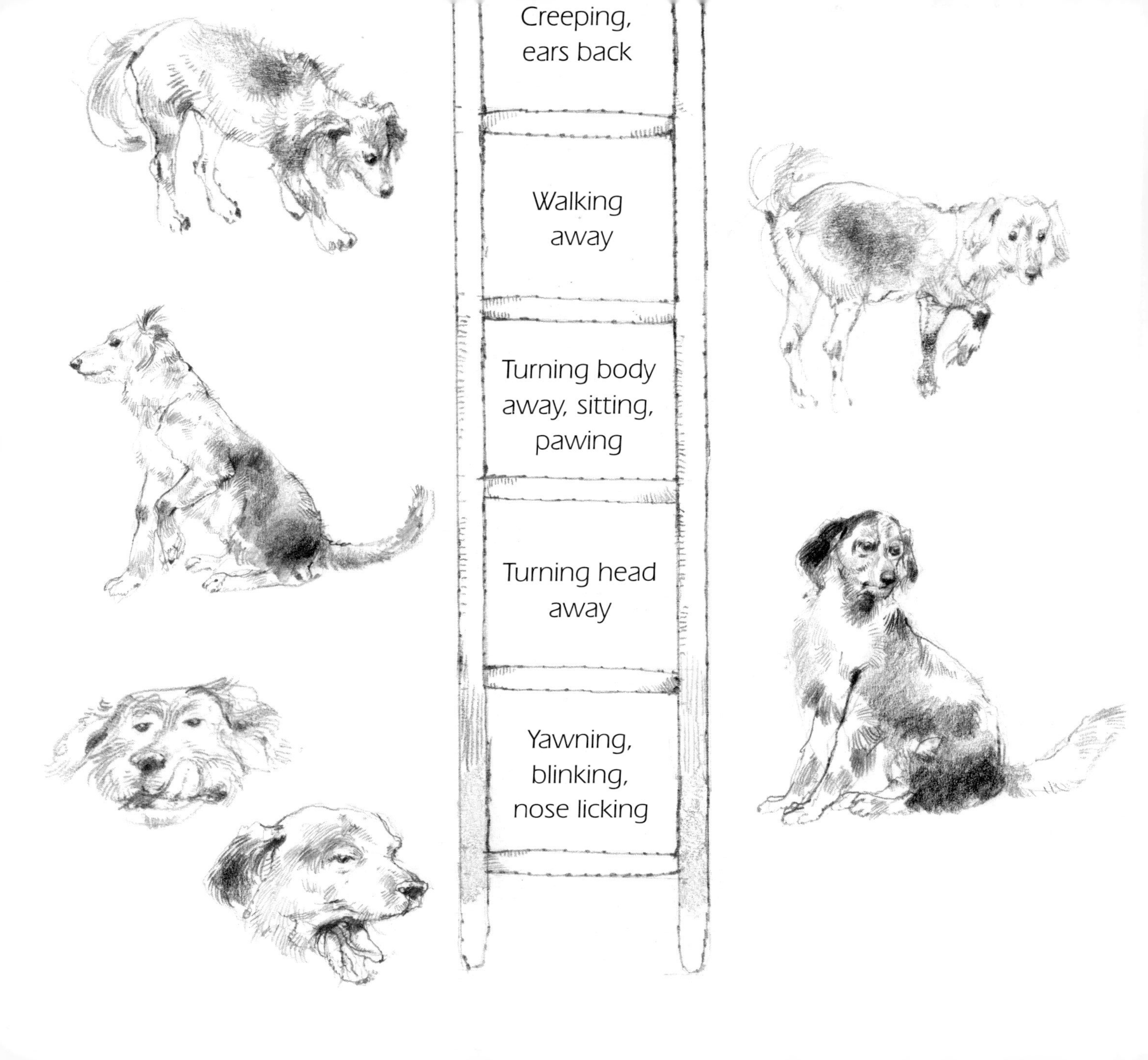
Creeping, ears back
Walking away
Turning body away, sitting, pawing
Turning head away
Yawning, blinking, nose licking

The Ladder of Aggression

Because they cannot speak, dogs do many things with their bodies to communicate to companions how they feel and what they want. The main purpose of all the gestures dogs use is to keep the peace. They do not want to have to fight with others any more than you do. Just as we will try to calm someone down who is upset or angry using words, dog will use their bodies. If a dog raises his paw, puts his ears back or walks away from you when you are upset or angry with him, he is trying to calm you down. Even if you are angry or arguing with someone else, he may do exactly the same thing as he is now trying to calm you both down. Dogs very often seem to us to look as if they know they have done something wrong when we are angry with them. But it is unlikely that they have the ability to feel guilty as we do. They are instead simply asking us to calm down and stop threatening them. If you continue to be angry with a dog despite his calming attempts, he may begin to feel like biting you to make you stop. Whereas you will use words in anger, a dog will use his teeth.

The Ladder of Aggression is an illustration of many of these gestures. They are used when dogs are in the company of either people or other dogs and they are all designed to try to reduce stress and avert danger, in effect to say, 'Please stay calm!' or even, 'Go away and leave me alone!' How many of these gestures can you remember being described in the Canine Commandments and what did they all mean? The lower rungs on this ladder are the equivalent of polite social gestures that humans use, such as smiling, saying hello and shaking hands. These are things we do to let other people know we want to be friendly towards them and mean them no harm. We expect similar gestures in return so that we can all remain at ease with people, whether we know them well or not. It is just the same for dogs.

If our smile or handshake were to be met with disapproval or anger, it would without doubt start to make us feel upset and rather less like being friendly. Exactly the same is true for dogs. If lower rungs of the ladder do not seem to work, dogs are forced further up towards the top and to have to growl and bite. Unfortunately, by misunderstanding what a dog is trying to say with his body, we often accidentally make them feel much less friendly towards us. Getting angry with a dog for walking away from us rather than coming to us, or because he looks guilty about something he has done, will make a dog more likely to move up the ladder. He may even learn to go straight to the top of the ladder immediately just to be on the safe side. Remember above all that a dog who looks 'guilty' or 'sorry', is only asking you to calm down – **not** admitting that he has been naughty! The more angry we are however, and the more a dog tries to calm us down, the more guilty-looking he will seem to become. If we carry on being angry instead of calming down immediately, dogs will learn that the only behaviour which gets people to leave them alone is to bite.

The most useful way to make sure a dog is unlikely to bite you is to ask him to come to you, wherever he is and whether or not he has something in his mouth. If he runs happily towards you, he is saying that he feels safe in your company. If, however, he stays lying down, stands still or walks or runs away from you, he is trying to say the opposite – 'You are threatening me – please stay away!' If you follow him or try to touch him, you will show him that you do not understand his language and make him more likely to have to growl or bite.

None of us would enjoy being misunderstood or being unable to understand what people around us are saying. But this is how many of our dogs feel a lot of the time. Learning to understand what a dog is really trying to say and encouraging him to understand what you mean, but without getting angry, will make both of you very much happier.

Happy dogs have no need to bite.